Where does it belong?

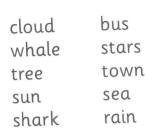

Read the words. Write each word in the correct shape.

cloud	bus	aeroplane	river
whale	stars	jellyfish	castle
tree	town	cow	spaceship
sun	sea	ship	pond
shark	rain	dog	rainbow

sky words

land words

water words

3

Recycling

Max always saves paper, glass and cans so that they can be recycled. He takes them to a recycling centre and puts them into different containers.

Draw lines to show where the objects go.

Finish the sentence

Read the story.
Draw a ring round the answer that completes the last sentence.

The house is in the garden. It has a bowl of water and a carrot inside it. The house belongs to

some birds   a cat   a rabbit

There is a small pond in the garden.
An animal hops into the water.
It eats flies and is green. The animal is a

fish   frog   tortoise

My name is Scrap. I sleep in a house in the back yard. There is a bone outside it. I am a

horse   dog   pig

Daisy lives in a field. She is a big, black-and-white animal and eats grass. She is a

crocodile   cow   polar bear

Where have they been?

Read the sentences above the pictures. Draw a circle round the picture which tells you where everybody has visited.

Mum took the twins out one evening. They saw a triangle, a trumpet, a violin and some drums.
They must have gone to a...

Jon and his family went out for the day. They saw elephants, lions and monkeys. They must have visited the...

Urvashi and Tariq spent Saturday enjoying sport. They saw wickets, bats, a ball and an umpire. They must have been at a...

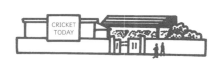  

Daniel and Becky enjoyed travelling. On their journey they could hear the wind blowing and the water lapping. They must have been on a...

Who's who?

Read the sentences.
Write the correct name under each picture. Think carefully!

Harriet feeds the birds in the garden.

Jake swims in the sea.

Olivia reads her book in the garden.

Harry feeds birds in the park.

Emily enjoys swimming in the pool.

Henry reads space books in the library.

What does not belong?

Look at the pictures.
Read the sentences.
Cross out the sentence that does not belong.

Horse riding

Polly fell off the swing.

Jason mounted his pony.

Kevvy gave Dobbin a carrot.

Sports Day

Talib won the sack race.

Lisa won the egg-and-spoon race.

Emma had a bath.

At the gym

Michael was on the exercise bike.

Tim played the piano.

Linda enjoyed the rowing machine.

The football match

Dad climbed a mountain.

Jamie headed the ball.

The goalie caught the ball.

Choosing a dog

Alice and Ben went to the dogs' home to choose a new dog. They saw a white dog with black spots called Gus, and a small dog called Jock with a collar and lead. Lucky was a big brown dog without a collar. Kim was playing with a red ball. Lottie was wearing a pink bow.

Answer these questions.

1. What is the name and colour of the biggest dog?

    _____

2. Which dog has a collar and lead? _____

3. One of the dogs is wearing a pink ribbon.
    Which one? _____

4. What colour is Kim's ball? _____

5. Which dog isn't wearing a collar? _____

6. Which dog would you choose? _____

What happens next?

Read the story carefully.
Decide what happens next and circle the correct picture.

 Flora planted some seeds. She scattered them on the soil.

What happens next?

 Dylan loves to watch videos. He buys one every time he is given some money. His Aunt gave him £10.
What happens next?

 Daisy's puppy chewed books and he even chewed a cushion. Dad said the puppy had to sleep in his kennel. Daisy left her trainers on the grass.
What happens next?

 Stefan said he would wash the dishes. He turned on the taps just as his mobile rang. He spoke to his friend!
What happens next?

10

Read all about it!

Read the newspaper.
Colour the circle beside the sentence that tells you the main idea.

Mid Week News

Karate Club

this week
Monday and
Saturday

○ No karate
this week.

○ Karate meets
twice this week.

○ Someone
wants to buy
a computer
and a printer.

○ Someone
wants to sell
a computer
and a printer.

FOR SALE

Computer and
colour printer

Wanted
Dog walker to walk
Frisky every day
except Sunday.

○ A dog walker is needed on Sunday.

○ A dog walker is needed every day
except Sunday.

Garden Open
Saturdays and Sundays
2 o'clock until 5 o'clock

○ Garden closed at weekends.

○ Garden open at weekends.

○ The robbers
were caught.

○ Two bank
robbers got
away.

○ Everything
costs 30p.

○ Pay 30p to
go into car
boot sale.

Car Boot Sale
in aid of Dogs for
the Blind

Entry 30p

How does it end?

Read each story.
Colour in the circle next to the correct endings.

Ellen found her trousers and jumper too tight and her trainers hurt her toes. What has happened?

○ Ellen has become shorter.

○ Ellen is wearing her older sister's clothes.

○ Ellen has grown.

Toby found it hard to read his book. He held it nearer to his eyes but he still found it difficult to read. What is wrong?

○ The book is closed.

○ Toby needs glasses.

○ The book is boring.

Jamie went to a party. He ate four sausage rolls, a plate of curry and six ice-creams. What happened next?

○ He had a plate of chilli.

○ He went to a disco.

○ He felt very sick.

Laura was skiing when she hit a tree! She was unable to move. She cried for help! What happened next?

○ She rolled down the mountain.

○ She was airlifted by helicopter.

○ She slept overnight in the snow.

Where are they?

Read the sentences carefully, then colour the cats the correct colour.

1. The black cat lies on the roof.

2. The ginger cat is in the tree.

3. The black-and-white cat is between the black cat and the ginger cat.

4. The striped cat is below the black-and-white cat.

5. The grey cat is behind the hedge near the door.

6. The grey-and-white cat lies on the gate.

7. The brown cat walks along the fence.

8. The ginger-and-white cat is next to the brown cat.

What will happen next?

Read the sentence.
Write what **you** think will happen next.

Freddie dropped his glass.

The _____

Lucy wrote a letter to her friend.

She _____

Aidan fell into a muddy puddle.

He _____

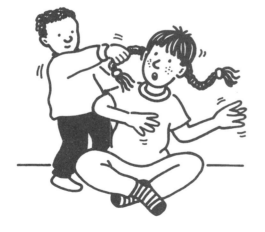

James pulled Jessica's hair.

She _____

Mark bowled a fast ball.

It _____

Which book?

Octavia and Jeremy went to the library to find the answers to their quiz sheet.
Which books did they use?

 1 FAIRY STORIES

 2 FAMOUS BUILDINGS

 3 INSECTS

 4 ALL ABOUT HORSES

 5 MUSICAL INSTRUMENTS

 6 EXPLORING SPACE

 7 Garden Birds

 8 TOYS

Quiz Sheet

- [ ] Name the bird with a red breast.
- [ ] Which minibeast makes honey?
- [ ] Where does the British Parliament meet?
- [ ] Which planets orbit the earth?
- [ ] Which large instrument is plucked?
- [ ] What is a yo-yo?
- [ ] What is a stallion?
- [ ] Which bird laid 'golden eggs'?

What will they do?

Read each sentence.
Colour in the circle next to what they will do.

Sita wrote a thank-you letter to her aunt.

○ She phoned her aunt on her mobile.

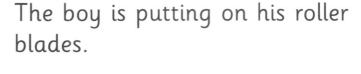

○ She posted the letter.

The boy is putting on his roller blades.

○ He will go roller blading.

○ He will go cycling.

Jo Jo went to the library.

○ She chose a book.

○ She had fish and chips.

Simon took his dog to the vet.

○ The vet gave the dog an injection.

○ The dog gave the vet an injection.

How does it end?

Read the story.
Draw a circle round what happens next.

It is very cold tonight. It has snowed all day. Dad goes outside and collects some logs. He finds some matches and paper. What will he do?

   light a fire   cook the dinner

We went to the beach. We swam in the sea and built sand-castles. Mum took some money out of her bag. What was she going to buy?

ice-cream   soup   cheese   a comb

Mr Smith enjoys digging his garden. He plants seeds every spring. They grow into

chickens   vegetables   crisps   paper

Mrs Smith went Christmas shopping. She bought a present for her children. She came home with

a cinema   a fairground   a computer   a park

Come to the pantomime!

43 Green Lane, Tindale, London SC1 DS3
12 December 2009

Dear Cara,

    Mum has five tickets for the pantomime, Cinderella. We are going on Saturday 19th December. It starts at 3 o'clock.

    Dad, Mum, Tom and I will be going. Please come with us.

    I am very excited. Cinderella will be wearing a beautiful gown at the ball. Perhaps we can go on stage at the end and have some fun.

    Hope to see you on Saturday.

    With Love from
    Lily

Underline the correct answers.

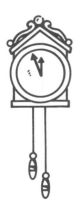
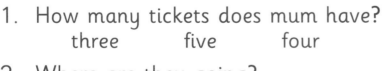

1. How many tickets does mum have?
    three   five   four

2. Where are they going?
    to a circus   to a football match   to a pantomime

3. When does it start?
    3 o'clock   half-past 3   4 o'clock

4. What will Cinderella be wearing?
    jeans   a beautiful gown   a bikini

5. Who wrote the letter?
    Cara   Lily   Tom

6. What might they do?
    go on stage   eat spaghetti   pick flowers

Why do you think Lily is so excited?

_____

Because!

Read each story. Colour in the circle beside the sentence which tells you more details about the story.

Mrs Green travels into town by bus on Tuesdays. She goes to the market to buy fish. Today is Tuesday. Mrs Green is at the market because

- ○ she meets a friend there.
- ○ she wants some cod.
- ○ she sees a pretty dress.

My dog is black and brown. He barks when people come to the door. He is barking now because

- ○ he wants to go outside.
- ○ he is hungry.
- ○ the postman rings the doorbell.

Everyone on Woodlands School football team wears a red shirt on Saturdays. It is Saturday and Marcus is wearing a red shirt because

- ○ he cannot find his green shirt.
- ○ he is on the football team.
- ○ he always wears red shirts.

Kofi saw a red and green parrot at the zoo. The parrot always talks when he sees people. He is talking now because

- ○ he has seen Kofi and his friends.
- ○ he wants some water.
- ○ he is hungry.

Bike for sale!

FOR SALE

Please buy my super bike!
It's a green mountain bike with 12 speeds!
My bike is only 2 years old and has new tyres and saddle.

£75 for a quick sale!
(Money needed for holidays)

Contact Euan on 017 836294

Answer the questions.
Draw a circle round the correct answer.

Has the bike new tyres?	yes	no
Does the bike cost £55?	yes	no
Is this a For Sale poster?	yes	no
Does the bike belong to Ella?	yes	no
Is the bike 5 years old?	yes	no
Is the money needed for holidays?	yes	no
Do you contact the owner by phone?	yes	no

Reward!

LOST DOG

Bodge is a small black dog with a white face, white paws and a short black tail.
Last seen in Goose Green Park.

If found ring 01975 4623

REWARD!

Draw a circle round the correct answers.

1. What is this?

birthday card   poster   comic

2. What is it for?

to sell a dog   to give a dog away   to find a lost dog

3. What colour is the dog?

white   black   black and white

4. What is the dog's name?

Dodge   Bodge   Bodger

5. What is the name of the park?

Goose Green Park   Green Park   Goose Park

6. Which dog is lost? _____

Ezra the elephant

Ezra was the smallest elephant in the zoo. However, he was very upset when the other elephants teased him calling him "Titch".

One night, when all the elephants were asleep, Ezra awoke to the smell of smoke. The elephant shelter was on fire.

Ezra ran to the moat, he filled his trunk with water and squirted it on the burning shelter until the fire was out.

Ezra was the hero and the other elephants never, ever teased him again!

Read the story. Write 1, 2, 3, 4 or 5 in the boxes to number the sentences in the order they happened in the story.

☐ The elephant shelter was on fire.

☐ Ezra was the hero.

☐ Ezra awoke to the smell of smoke.

☐ The other elephants teased him.

☐ He filled his trunk with water.

Why do you think Ezra was called "Titch"?

_____

Give the reasons

Read each story. Choose the ending which fits best. Colour the square next to it.

It was a very hot and sunny day. Fiona and her friend went on the lake in a boat. When she got home her face, arms and legs were very red. Why did Fiona look like this?

☐ It was a windy day.
☐ She was wearing some of mum's make-up.
☐ She was sunburned.

Grandad tried to read his paper. He held it nearer to his eyes. He screwed up his eyes but still he couldn't read it.
What was wrong?

☐ The paper was written in French.
☐ He was wearing sunglasses.
☐ He was wearing grandma's glasses.

Harriet enjoys working in her garden. She likes fresh vegetables because they make salads taste so much better. Harriet is making a salad for her mum and dad.
What will she do?

☐ She will buy vegetables from a greengrocer.
☐ She will use her home-grown vegetables.
☐ She will buy a carton of salad from the supermarket.

The Beeches News

Parents are planning to improve the school grounds.
There will be a sand-pit for the youngest children. Older children will have a football pitch, a grassed area for ball games, a jungle climbing frame and a running track.

All the children will use benches in the playground.
Trees will be planted for shade.

The children will sow wild flower seeds.
There is great excitement about these plans. The work will start in August.

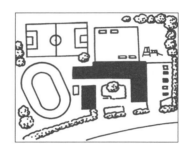

Read the story. Write 1, 2, 3, 4, 5 or 6 in the boxes to number the sentences in the order they happened in the story.

☐ The children will sow wild flower seeds.

☐ The work will start in August.

☐ Parents are planning to improve the school grounds.

☐ Older children will have a football pitch.

☐ All the chidren will use benches in the playground.

☐ There will be a sand-pit for the youngest children.

What would you like in your school grounds?

_____

Zak's dream

Look at the picture.
Read the Story.

Zak was fast asleep. He dreamt he was swimming in a river. Suddenly, a huge crocodile swam towards him. It was green with enormous yellow teeth. As he swam nearer, the crocodile opened his mouth. It was like a large cave. Zak was terrified! All at once he awoke! It was only a dream!

Underline the correct answer.

What did Zak dream about?
a kangaroo   a crocodile   an alligator

What was Zak doing in his dream?
riding his bike   feeding a crocodile at the zoo   swimming

What was the animal like?
green with   yellow with   green with
small teeth   green teeth   yellow teeth

What did the animal's mouth look like?
a large cave   a little cave   a big hole

How did Zak feel when the animal swam near him?
happy   pleased   terrified

Friends

Read this letter.

The Orchard,
Wood Lane,
Newport
Saturday 3rd August

Dear Finn,
I hope you are happy in your new home in Westport. I have missed playing football with you. Do you have a new friend to play with? Our new neighbours do not have any children. Please come and stay soon.
Your very best friend,
Amos

Draw a ring round the sentence which is true.

Finn lives next door.	Finn lives in Westport.	Finn lives in Newport.
I enjoy playing alone.	I have a new playmate.	I have missed playing with you.
The new neighbours don't have children.	The new neighbours have a dog.	The new neighbours have two children.
Amos wrote the letter in April.	Finn wrote the letter in August.	Amos wrote the letter in August.

Award!

Award for Ashdown School

Pupils delivered letters to houses in Ashdown. The letters asked for Children's books and the local people handed in hundreds of books.

The mayor presented the school with a shield.

Ashdown School won an award for helping the children of Gambia in Africa.

Read all about it!
Tick the box ✔ to show the correct answer.

How did Jack hear about this?
in a book ☐   on TV ☐   in a newspaper ☐

What is the title of this report?
Ashdown School ☐   Pupils delivered letters ☐
Award for Ashdown School ☐

What did the children do?
read books ☐   collect books ☐   go to the library ☐

Where were the books sent?
Ghana ☐   Guinea ☐   Gambia ☐

What was presented to the children?
a shield ☐   a certificate ☐   a medal ☐

Map reading

Take your pencil for a walk!

1. Start at the church and turn right into Hill Street.
2. Walk down Hill Street to the fire station and cross the road to Primrose Path.
3. Turn right and walk along Primrose Path until you reach Baker Street.
4. Walk up Baker Street turning left into Church Road.
5. Walk on to The Green until you reach _____

What can you see? _____

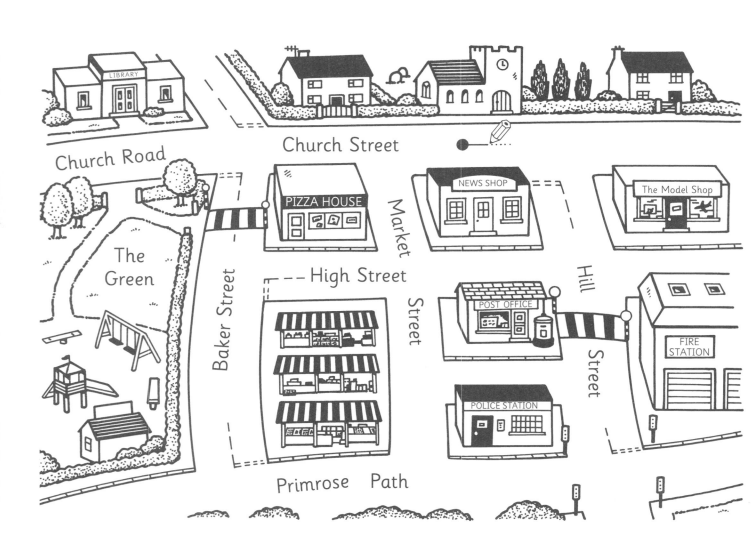

What else did you see on your walk? _____

Headlines

Read each headline.
Circle the sentence that best fits the headline.

FALCON
Scott's Diary found in Antarctic

Husky dogs savaged penguins.

Ship wrecked by penguins.

Jan 18th: reached South Pole

JINGLES
Pop idols sing for needy.

Bank collects money.

The Dolly Mixtures sing for Oxfam.

Dolly Mixtures reach top of charts.

EXPLORER
NEW PLANET discovered

Astronauts fly to moon.

Rocket takes off to Mars.

Scientist views unknown planet through telescope.

ANIMAL NEWS
Elephants stampede

There is a circus in town.

Elephants escape from zoo.

People queue for elephant rides.

Honey bees

Bees make honey with nectar. They gather nectar from flowers. Bees visit hundreds of flowers. They suck up nectar with their tongues. The bees return to the hive with the nectar and give it to other bees. They turn the nectar into honey in their stomachs. The honey is stored in the honeycomb until it is needed to feed the Queen Bee.

Read the sentences below. Write 1, 2, 3, 4 or 5 in each box to tell the order in which bees make honey.

The honey is stored in the honeycomb until it is needed to feed the Queen Bee.

They turn the nectar into honey in their stomachs.
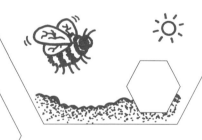

Bees make honey with nectar which they gather from flowers.
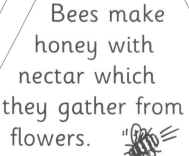

The bees return to the hive with nectar and give it to other bees.

They suck up the nectar with their tongues.